by construction companies and the gap that exists between them and *out-of-sector, best practice*. Widespread dissemination of the results should support an informed debate into how the performance of UK construction companies can be raised to a level of world class, best practice.

10. Overall, the results for the construction companies should be used as they were intended - to set the benchmarks for a process of continuous improvement. What they show is an industry that is coming to terms with the challenges and opportunities that IT presents. Rewards will not, however, be enjoyed without the kind of commitment shown by the example best practice. Development over time, with a clear strategy for the immediate and longer term future, is essential to succeeding in the changing world of construction into the next millennium.

Foreword

There are a great many ways in which an organisation can improve its performance. Benchmarking is one such way. Many industries have transformed themselves over the past decades by seeking radical and massive change in the way they went about their business. Few methods of highlighting these necessary changes have succeeded as well as benchmarking.

The construction industry claims a very special and distinct way of operating which does not lend itself to learning from other industries or indeed from within itself. The pivotal role of the client and his agents in the design of the end product and the well established processes in the industry prevent the degree of flexibility deemed necessary for the industry to change radically. If this were true then the UK industry must decline as foreign competitors enter the UK market, bringing with them differing and sometimes lower cost practices.

Equally, many industries have been unable to change themselves sufficiently quickly against foreign competition and have subsequently now become mere legends of bygone British Industry. IT has a very specific contribution to show what changes are possible. It is by examining how other, well respected industries have employed IT in some detail that opportunities are presented to the UK construction industry. It is these opportunities which this series of studies seeks to identify.

The benefits of comparing one's own performance with that of your competitors and those you most admire within and outside your own industry is now well proven. A great many of you will have undertaken this form of study before for your own organisation. This study differs in so far as eleven of the top construction companies in the UK participated in a single benchmark with the aim of lifting their own performance and that of the whole UK industry.

This report shows how the eleven participating companies fared against one another and how they all fared against an out-of-industry organisation. As we had asked companies to put their best site forward for benchmarking, the discrepancy between their differing degrees of use of IT has been surprising. These differences are also a testimony to the honesty of the participants and serve to highlight the additional potential IT can offer to those operating the construction sites.

This study seeks to start a debate on the use of IT in the construction site processes and to highlight an agenda against which other organisations can assess their own performance. The report will be updated in the future and will have an international addendum added in due course.

Within these pages I am confident you will find some fascinating conclusions, not least that there is a great deal of variation in the use of IT where you might assume that everyone is doing the same thing. If the objective of lifting the general performance of UK construction site processes through the better deployment of IT seems too distant to you, the nearer goal of how to beat the other guy is also available to you within this report.

David A. Smith
Construct IT, Management Board

1. Introduction

The Construct IT Centre of Excellence

The Centre is an industry-led network of major clients, consultants, contractors, suppliers, IT and communications companies and universities that has been set up to co-ordinate and promote IT research in construction in the UK. A list of member organisations current at the publication of this report is included as Appendix A.

The Centre's mission is to improve competitive performance of the UK construction industry. It will achieve this by informing the IT investments of companies in the industry and ensuring these IT investments remain well informed. Objectives include co-ordinating research, promoting innovation, continuous redefinition of an industry vision, forming links with similar international initiatives and establishing best current practice (DOE, 1995).

Background to the study

An important part of the published work plan for *The Centre* is the overseeing of projects designed to develop underlying technologies, principles and best practice. It is the last of these – best practice projects – which serves as the basis for this publication, the second in a series of benchmarking studies. The projects represent a crucial element in the UK construction industry's search for efficiency gains and cost savings.

Best practice projects aim to:

- measure the effectiveness with which IT is being used to support mission-critical business processes in major UK clients, consultants and construction companies;

- alert key construction industry executives to their company's relative position in terms of its use of IT for this purpose;

- highlight, via industry-related reports and seminars, examples of best practice in the use of IT within the construction and other industry sectors; and

- identify system development and research priorities for the future for action by other members of *The Centre*.

These aims arise because of the concern which surrounds the UK construction industry's use of IT. Senior managers within client, consultant and construction companies often fail to recognise how far the construction industry falls behind other sectors in its use of IT. Furthermore, there seems to be a lack of appreciation of how effective IT can be in supporting business processes or how research can encourage more effective use of IT. This report and its predecessor on *supplier management* is largely a response to these concerns.

By addressing each of the underlying issues, in an awareness-generating exercise, the report and those that follow can be used as a vehicle for stimulating technology transfer. This is achieved through a shared experience of best practice in both the construction industry and other industry sectors with which construction might be compared.

Scope of the study

Each best practice benchmarking project is devoted to mission-critical business processes.

Construction site processes were chosen because they are fundamental to the work of any construction company.

The construction site is a key area where money is made or lost and where there is considerable scope for improving efficiency, productivity and quality performance through appropriate uses of IT. In the report, *Constructing the Team,* Sir Michael Latham calls for a 30% real reduction in the cost of construction by the year 2000. Responses to his report have variously considered changes to ways in which construction projects are managed. Better management means better calibre managers whose time is optimised by systems and tools which provide information in a timely and cost effective way. As a tool of management, IT has to have a significant role to play in securing cost savings of the order advocated by Latham and, perhaps more importantly, a growing number of the industry's clients.

Construction site processes describes that combination of activities which turns basic resources into a finished product. This can range from organisation of the materials, labour and other resources on the site to activities which control the flows of information and finance. It is a complex business and one that is deserving of our attention. Benchmarking IT in construction site processes is long overdue.

The report sets out findings which, it is hoped, will enable construction companies to set an agenda for their own IT strategy for improved management of construction site processes. In the first instance, the results are intended to assist the eleven companies who gave their time and enthusiasm for the study. Anonymity for the companies has been preserved throughout this report.

Method of study

The study was based principally on structured interviews with site-based project personnel and IT managers of the companies. A questionnaire covering seven sets of activities and processes, containing in excess of 200 individual questions, was drafted by the research team. This was piloted with three volunteer companies and the feedback used to amend the form and content of some questions. Eleven companies were then asked to participate in the main study by nominating their best site from an IT perspective. The results have been analysed and are presented here.

The approach has relied upon self-evaluation by the companies in responding to the questions put at interview. Under this arrangement, it is always possible for a company to offer less than honest answers. The research team is confident that the answers are a true and accurate statement of the companies' use and attitude towards IT at the site level. The purpose of benchmarking is intended to lead a company to identifying and adopting improved business processes. To do so requires an assessment of how the company performs presently in its mission-critical processes. Distorting that assessment would not necessarily help the search for improvement.

Whilst the results are useful for the companies and others with an interest in construction site processes, they are indicative only of current practice within the group of companies participating in the study. A more meaningful approach and one that is implicit in benchmarking is to compare performance with another or other companies, outside the domain of study, that might be regarded as exemplars of best practice. By doing this, it is possible to measure the distance by which those within construction fall short of best practice and to provide insights which might help them close the gap.

The responses obtained from the eleven companies have been analysed and the results compared with a company achieving best practice in an adjacent industrial sector. As far as practicable, individual company responses are presented without amendment. The basis for comparison is discussed in *Section 4*.

Target readership

The target readership for this report is chief executives and strategic business unit managers of construction companies. In the first instance, the report is restricted to the subject construction companies and other members of *The Centre*. The ultimate readership is, however, far wider.

Structure of the report

Section 2 – **Benchmarking Best Practice** introduces this important tool for business process reengineering. The broader context of the subject is discussed, in particular the strategic importance of IT to the business. Examples are given of how benchmarking has been applied in sectors other than construction and how it works in practice.

Section 3 – **The Search for Best Practice** considers IT use in adjacent sectors to construction where the function and discipline of project management is firmly established. The search for best practice IT leads us to an engineering-construction company. Here, processes are IT-enabled and integrated to an extent that is, so far,

Section 4 – **Eleven Construction Companies Compared** presents the results of the benchmarking study of the leading UK construction companies, in terms of relative positioning and in comparison with best practice. Each company's use of IT is assessed and supported, wherever possible, by comment or explanation. Companies' comments are ordered according to their performance under

each of seven areas. The section is prefaced by an assessment of the companies' overall performance and a measure of the degree of integration of their IT in supporting site activities and processes.

Section 5 – **Conclusions** bring together the lessons which have been learned from the study. Recommendations for developing effective IT in support of construction site processes and future research priorities are included.

2. Benchmarking Best Practice

The purpose of this section is to show why benchmarking should be an appropriate tool for management in the construction industry and how it can be used by anyone with a serious enough intention to do so. Examples of its application in sectors other than construction are provided.

A tool to support business process reengineering

Competition provides an impetus for improvement. Benchmarking provides a tool for continuous improvement. Today's best practice will not be tomorrow's, that is why the process has to be continuous. In increasingly tough marketplaces, companies have to know how they can perform better and at lower cost. Competitors provide the challenge and they can also provide the insights into how performance can be raised and costs driven down. Survival today is about learning from others who are better, though they need not all be one's competitors. Useful lessons can and are being learned by companies who have compared themselves with others in different industries. Recognition that businesses and sectors rarely, if ever, suffer uniquely means that comparison with *best-in-class* or *world class performers,* wherever they are, can raise the prospect of a greater market share and higher profits.

If the question of survival is of strategic importance to a business and benchmarking can be shown to be key to that survival then it has to be of strategic importance. Though survival is not the goal of benchmarking, competitive excellence is and should be the driving force for continuous improvement.

During the 1990s, businesses have increasingly focused on the needs of their clients and customers and the extent to which they satisfy them. Whilst this is clearly necessary, it is not everything. Clients exercise primary interest in the end product or service and companies look upon their suppliers as the means to help deliver that end product. The point is, however, that businesses need to consider their core processes if they are to deliver against increasingly demanding client and customer needs (LEIBFRIED AND MCNAIR, 1994). In this context, it is important to consider all organisations and people who have a stake in the survival of the company. These stakeholders, as they are known, include owners, employees, suppliers, clients and customers. They depend on one another and because relationships consume resources, costs are incurred. Management of these relationships is necessary from an accounting perspective since cash flow is the lifeblood of most organisations. Benchmarking can provide management with the tools needed to make decisions about policies and practices in regard to what has to be one of, if not, the most fundamental of processes to a construction company. Managing construction site processes – or construction project management – has to become more competitive if companies are to thrive. Clients and customers are looking for greater efficiencies and lower costs, that is why sites have become the target for study.

The thrust of this study is one that identifies with the practicalities, not the theory of benchmarking. Elsewhere in the UK construction industry, benchmarking studies are under way. Individual clients such as BAA and consortia, under initiatives such as the *Reading Construction Forum* and others representing a cross-section of the industry, are studying the means for deriving benchmarks. Cost, time and quality have become the targets for studies in construction. Some are closely tied to a given form of construction or type of building, since the studies are funded in large measure by clients with particular interests. These very same clients are themselves active in benchmarking. Airports, supermarkets, banks etc. are having to compete for business and are seeking continuous improvement. These clients do not see why construction should be a special case.

Benchmarking in practice

Benchmarking is objective competitive analysis. Its main purpose is to measure a company's product or service, and the business processes which support them, against the company's goals and aspirations, its competitors and *best-in-class* companies in other industries.
It is *"an external focus on internal activities, functions or operations in order to achieve continuous improvement"* (LEIBFRIED AND MCNAIR, 1994).

A benchmarking study begins with an analysis of existing activities and practices within the company. These processes have to be properly understood and measurable before comparison can take place with an external company. Usually, benchmarking is a *one-on-one* activity; that is, it is used by one company to help identify improvements in its own processes by exchanging information in a workshop with another company. Normally, the activity is of mutual benefit.

An obvious observation is that it surely cannot be possible to look so closely at one's competitors. Yet this is precisely what is happening. Moreover, it is not unknown in construction circles. In partnering arrangements – especially those where a client or customer is to share most of their business amongst a few select suppliers – the necessity of benchmarking becomes more apparent. Partnerships are implicitly about openness and communication. Furthermore, benchmarking is directed at technical or general managerial processes and so commercially sensitive information is unlikely to be exposed.

Setting objectives and goals which ensure competitive excellence strikes at the heart of performance measurement. Benchmarking is the means for identifying performance levels and provides the basis for continuous improvement. For it to work successfully, benchmarking has to be stakeholder driven, forward-looking, participative and focused on quality. A consequence is that it forces issues out into the open so that they can be dealt with according to the goals of the company. It identifies current practice and through external comparison identifies best practice and the actions that are needed to match and exceed that best practice. By bringing in the external dimension, energy can be channelled away from internal conflict towards a focus on achieving the competitive edge.

Applications in other industry sectors

The Japanese approach enshrined in kaizen tells us that improvement is an ongoing process and involves everyone. Few people would not acknowledge the colossal success of Japanese industry, built on the principle of gradual, unending improvement, doing things a little better and setting, then achieving, higher standards. Much of the incentive for benchmarking in the west stems from the success and subsequent domination of Japanese industry in world markets. Yet whole industries failed to perceive the threat of Japanese industry in the 1960s and 1970s. The gradual improvement in productivity, quality and service was no short term accident. It was a consequence of a culture that had to rebuild itself.

Credit for bringing benchmarking to the attention of the western business world belongs to Xerox Corporation, through their response to the threat of Japanese competition in the late 1970s. It is widely held that, without a radical shift in thinking and behaviour, Xerox would probably have not survived: at least not in their present form. At the time, Xerox were faced with competition from Canon who were able to offer comparable copiers for less than Xerox could manufacture them. Like so many others, Xerox could not afford to wait a couple of decades to take the slow, but proven, path trodden by the Japanese. Short-cuts that would allow them to compete and stay in business were called for. Benchmarking was the response to that need. Soon, it reduced costs by 50% and defects to levels comparable with Japanese industrial products.

Since then, benchmarking has grown to become part of the tool-kit of management in companies across the world. Examples in banking, retailing, air transportation, automotive manufacture, communications and IT provide evidence that it is no isolated activity. Conditions which typically trigger the need for benchmarking include:

- quality programmes (British Airways plc);

- cost reduction/budget process (IBM);

- operations improvements (Exxon Chemical);

- new ventures (Toyota–Lexus); and

- competitive assaults/crises (Xerox).

With one exception, these are examples of reactions to events rather than a response to the need to assess the company's performance continuously.

Nevertheless, they provide sufficient incentive for management to bring about a re-evaluation of business processes.

Benchmarking is not, however, something which is directed solely at high profile or cost significant processes: it has application almost everywhere in an organisation. Many minor business processes are subjected to study in myriad organisations. Enough of them will make a mark on overall product or service delivery. This can mean more profit instead of unnecessary cost.

Conclusions

This section has discussed how benchmarking has a central place in providing management with a tool for continuous improvement. Its success in industries across the world is testament to this. The idea that one should be committed to finding better ways at lower cost could hardly be described as novel. That benchmarking should be a relative latecomer to construction is unfortunate, but it is not too late to make a major impact.

3. The Search for Best Practice

Benchmarking is the opportunity for companies to review their business processes. Internal examination may provide part of the answer, but it could never provide it all. For benchmarking to mean anything – and for it to live up to its name – requires objective competitive analysis through comparison with external organisations. Comparison between companies competing in the same sector and across industries provides that objectivity. This section considers the rationale behind this *"external focus on internal activities"*.

Wider benefits from benchmarking in construction

For construction companies – many of whom offer capacity as opposed to a product or *productised* service – the need for benchmarking is perhaps greater than in the manufacturing case. In the latter, goods or products can be objectively compared, one against another, along with the processes that create them. Understanding how to do things better is more readily apparent. Construction offers no such transparency and relies on procedures and practices which are often ill-defined and poorly documented. From a client and customer perspective, differentiation between construction companies is not always easy. Lowest bid price is often the only way of choosing one company over another.

Between 1992 and the present, the price of construction work has dropped by around 26%. A proportion of the saving so far can be attributed to market forces: margins have been cut everywhere. But this cannot account for the total figure. Some structural change must have taken place. Reductions in layers of management may have been the rapid response by some companies, as a way of reducing overheads and raising competitiveness. This action is not necessarily a consequence of considered plans which strive to increase efficiency whilst lowering operating costs. Survival has played a large part, as time does not permit gradual changes to take place. Short-cuts are therefore needed and, again, this is where benchmarking has a part to play.

The marketplace for construction is likely to suffer from over-capacity for some time. When competition is greatest, as at this time, pressure on prices is downwards. On its own, this should be significant reason to begin benchmarking in earnest. The traditions within the industry do, however, militate against this. Commercial considerations tend to overrule most other considerations. When companies are struggling to survive, few managers are going to want to appear to be asking for their systems and processes to be opened up to competitors. Streamlined business processes would surely benefit any company – through lower overheads – and provide competitive edge. The gains might, however, be relatively short lived. If one were to accept that the competition would soon catch up, so to speak, then companies really do have to recognise the need for continuous improvement. This is why benchmarking is so important and the scope for its application extensive.

A further argument for construction to be considered for benchmarking is that if ever there were an industry or sector that needed objective measures (or benchmarks), this has to be a prime candidate. The industry and its clients suffer because there are too few measures; cost being the notable exception. This absence gets in the way of improving the processes to deliver better end products. A lack of understanding of the relationship between quality and price – something that manufacturing has grasped and succeed with – is all too evident. Clients and customers simply do not know how much they ought to be paying for construction services, except as little as possible. Issues of value must come into play. Since the quality:price relationship is not properly understood, clients may be unable to judge whether or not they have achieved value for money. Benchmarking has the potential to change this position.

Out-of-sector comparisons

If construction companies are concerned about benchmarking against their competitors, they can and should consider joining, as in this instance, a group of like-minded companies in a confidential, non-attributable study. In any event, the study attracts more value and greater benefits if it is extended to *out-of-sector* examples of best practice. After all, there is little point in measuring how far one is adrift from competitors if they are all a long way from best practice.

Within this study, there is a place for comparison with *out-of-sector* companies. A difficulty arises, however, in selecting valid comparisons. Whilst similar construction companies can be compared and measured against a notion of what constitutes best practice, this cannot take the place of credible examples drawn from outside construction. Accordingly, the research team spent a significant amount of time addressing the issue of a valid comparison. Team members were mindful of the lack of acceptability of some industry sectors with which to draw comparison. The decision was taken to consider the

merits of a number of diverse industries on as an objective basis as possible. The sectors considered were: process plant engineering-construction, nuclear power station construction or reactor decommissioning, aircraft manufacture and the Channel Tunnel trains.

See Table 1: *on page 14*

This led us to identify an engineering-construction company for the *out-of-sector, best-in-class* comparison as it is one that specialises in both process plant engineering-construction and nuclear reactor refurbishment. The company's development of an integrated systems' approach is the principal feature that sets it apart from other contenders. Moreover, construction's *Achilles' heel* is its fragmentation and disjointed approach to construction project management. Success is usually determined by the quality of people and the effectiveness with which they work as teams. Recognising this characteristic as important is also to recognise integration. In this respect, we see integration as largely to do with bringing people closer together. Technology undoubtedly helps, but it is still only a support or prop for an essentially human activity. At the end of the day, successful projects are borne of successful teams. Having the right tools to support the team is a critical factor.

Best-in-class engineering-construction company

The company identified as *best-in-class* describes itself as a master builder in the engineering-construction industry. It is continually seeking ways to deliver top value and to do so through the development of the best tools to do work better, cheaper and faster. The company takes a global view of engineering-construction and means to do business wherever it can using technology to automate as much of its business processes

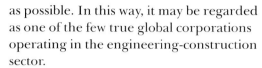

as possible. In this way, it may be regarded as one of the few true global corporations operating in the engineering-construction sector.

Over many years, the company has worked hard at developing an integrated family of automated tools to support the diversity of its activities both on and off site. It has been a major innovator in the use of CAD as a tool to aid construction, in addition to its more obvious and accepted role as a design aid. Integration is at the heart of the company's IT strategy. Its development plans show how determined it is to pull together the otherwise fragmented and disparate working that characterises most of the engineering-construction industry the world over. This commitment to integration is no accident nor is it simply a fashionable term with which to entice clients and customers.

The company's family of automation tools provides:

- information management systems that control and monitor labour and material costs, performance, progress against programme and contracts, as well as supporting risk assessment and trend analysis;

- materials management systems that track materials and components throughout the project to ensure *just-in-time* delivery;

- 3-D modelling systems, including simulation and real-time animated visualisation, to bring concept designs to life;

- computer-aided engineering (CAE) software to analyse and evaluate engineering designs for cost and programme implications;

- procurement systems that are linked electronically to both the project's systems and those of the company's major suppliers; and

- construction software to assess buildability and work sequencing.

In all of its work, the company emphasises its commitment to meeting client and customer objectives expressed in terms of time, cost and quality.

Conclusions

Finding an external organisation against which to benchmark is rarely easy and open to question as to the real motives behind a decision. For the purpose of this study, we have chosen engineering-construction because its business processes are so similar to those in building and civil engineering as to make comparison meaningful. Moreover, construction site processes are such an amalgam of different activities that to find a direct correspondence elsewhere, in another industry, is unlikely. By choosing an engineering-construction company, we have found a near perfect match, yet one that has sufficient specialisation to differentiate it from our more generalist within-industry group.

Table 1: Non-construction sectors compared

Note. (+) implies a characteristic which is shared in some way with the construction industry; conversely, (–) implies something that is inconsistent with the construction industry.

Process Plant Engineering-Construction

(+)	Made to order or project-specific
(+)	Major capital works
(+)	Use of IT in all stages of design and construction
(+)	Project management discipline is well-advanced
(+)	Contracted to build the end-product
(+)	Safety (a dimension of quality) is important
(–)	End-product worthless without certification of fitness for purpose

Nuclear Power Station Construction or Reactor Decommissioning

(+)	Made to order or project-specific
(+)	Major capital works
(+)	Use of IT in all stages of design and construction
(+)	Project management discipline is well-advanced
(+)	Contracted to build the end-product
(–)	Safety (a dimension of quality) is paramount
(–)	End-product worthless without certification of fitness for purpose

Aircraft Manufacture

(+)	Major capital items, increasingly customised
(+)	Use of IT in all stages of design and manufacture
(+)	Project management discipline has supplanted factory production ethos
(+)	Components sourced from across the world
(=)	Emphasis on teamwork within a design-build organisation
(–)	Safety (a dimension of quality) is paramount
(–)	End-product worthless without certification of fitness for purpose

Channel Tunnel Trains (Eurostar, Le Shuttle and Class 92 Locomotive)

(+)	Major capital items
(+)	Involved major innovations and procured against cost rather than quality
(–)	Short runs of similar, if not identical, rolling stock
(–)	Lack of useful IT reference material/case studies
(–)	Contracted to build the end-product

4. Eleven Construction Companies Compared

This section outlines the main results of the study, in which the use of IT in managing construction site processes by eleven construction companies is compared. The results reveal the current extent to which those contractors use IT and the importance they attach to that use. Each of six sets of applications within the overall process is considered and the results shown graphically. In addition, questions of a more general nature covering strategy, policy and procedures provide valuable insights into the companies' practices and experiences. By measuring the difference between themselves and their competitors, and by reference to *best practice IT,* individual companies can more easily see where the scope exists for improvement. For the purpose of the study and this report, IT is deemed to cover all electronic systems for capturing, storing, manipulating, retrieving and transmitting data and is not confined to computer-based equipment.

Basis of the comparisons, interviews and questionnaire

Eleven national construction companies took part in the study over a six months' period. They are amongst the leading companies in the UK. Any one company would probably regard most of the other ten as competitors. That factor did not deter any from taking part. Interviewees generally regarded the study as a worthwhile exercise and were keen to participate and, ultimately, to obtain the results. Confidentiality has been preserved throughout by the research team and anonymity is maintained for the companies in the results presented in this section.

The selection criterion for the benchmark was simple: nominate the best project site from an IT perspective. This could be anything within building and civil engineering. In the event, a wide range of projects were selected for visit by the study team. Structured interviews were arranged at which a detailed questionnaire was used to elicit answers to more than 200 questions. Interviews lasted on average two and a half hours and were concluded to the satisfaction of the research team and, generally, the interviewees. Apart from answers to pre-determined questions, interviewees were encouraged to offer comments wherever they felt this would add something to the quality of the answers. Interviewees were a mix of personnel drawn from the sites and IT managers. It was usual for two or three people to attend the interview from the companies and contribute to the discussions.

The questionnaires were designed around a generic model of construction site processes and tested on three construction companies in the first instance. All companies in the main study, irrespective of their size and operational procedures, were able to identify with the six areas of construction site processes: managing, supervising and administering; commercial management; legal, health and safety; planning, monitoring and control; delivery and materials' handling; and production on-site and off-site. Questions were divided into those associated with the use of IT for a given activity and those signifying the importance of the application of IT to that activity. Scoring questions were included in all sets of activities and processes.

Typically, these took the form of degrees of IT use and rating of importance of IT. Open questions accompanied each set so that qualitative comments and other factors could be recorded.

The questions covered the following.

Strategy, policy and procedures.
This considered, *inter alia,* the business and operational benefits of IT; basis of the decision to use IT on site; networking of systems on site; extent of client intervention; status of sites in terms of responsibility for IT; policy for dealing with IT; access of site personnel to IT; and the extent of electronic flows of information between site and other locations.

Managing, supervising and administering. The use and importance of IT in supporting activities that are general to the running of a site were considered, including correspondence; minutes; RFIs; labour allocations; payroll; progress reporting; notices/claims; instructions; drawing register; and technical information.

Commercial management. This covered estimating; valuations, sub-contractor payments; variations; dayworks; cost–value reconciliation; final accounts; and cash flow.

Legal, health and safety. This considered safety policy; COSHH and CDM regulations; insurance; building regulations; British Standards; and Codes of Practice.

Planning, monitoring and control.
This covered all activities associated with project planning and scheduling, typically the production of Gantt charts; network analyses; method statements; resource levelling; progress reports; and exception reports.

Delivery and materials' handling. The activities associated with the management of deliveries and the subsequent handling of materials on site were covered, including requisitions; purchase orders;

material call off; GRNs; and plant returns.

Production on-site and off-site.
This considered activities supporting production, for instance QA plans and reports; contract terms; drawings, specifications; setting out; and measurement.

Companies were also asked to describe, as best they could, their impending plans for the use of IT in support of construction site processes. Finally, opportunity was given to each company to provide any further information which it deemed appropriate to the study.

A list of the issues addressed within the questionnaire is given in Appendix B.

Analysis of the results

Responses were analysed and a simple scoring system applied to those questions covering the key issues of use and importance of IT. Cardinal numbers were used and totalled to produce a score for each set of activities relative to use and importance. Additionally, the extent to which activities and processes were integrated and the overall integration of site processes with those in the head (or regional) office were determined.

Scores were weighted by a factor of 1.5 in the case of strategy, policy and procedures; commercial management; planning, monitoring and control; and integration. These were felt to be the more important issues from a business perspective. Conversely, other process areas, whilst considered important, were felt to be less prominent and therefore not so critical to business success.

Results for each set of activities have been plotted on a scatter graph. Maximum possible scores indicate *best practice IT,* as provided by the engineering-construction example. The same maxima have been used to fix the relative positioning of all construction companies.

The research team had previously considered carefully what might constitute *best practice IT.* After much discussion, it was decided that best practice should equate to the electronic exchange of information and integration of site activities and processes. These factors were reflected by the maximum score attainable under the appropriate questions. The identification of world class practice IT in engineering-construction is proof that *best practice IT* does exist and that, as such, it can provide a reliable benchmark for comparison. The sector's proximity to construction also means that it provides a credible comparison for those who might fail to accept the validity of comparison with an *out-of-sector* company that had few, if any, features in common with construction.

Companies are not identified by name, but each will be able to establish its position relative to others by inspection of the graphs and accompanying statements and comments. Additionally, each company has been given, in confidence, a marked up copy of the results showing its own position. It should not be possible, therefore, for any company to identify another from the information presented here.

In each of the following graphs, the symbol □ signifies the industry average. *Best practice IT,* as exemplified by the engineering-construction company, is identified by the maximum points attainable on both axes and denoted by the symbol △. Additionally, the area covered by the axes has been separated into four equal quadrants to enable system development and research priorities to be assessed – see later commentary in *Section 5.*

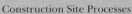

Overall Performance in the use of IT

Brief description

Assessment of the overall positions of all eleven construction companies relative to one another and best practice.

Results

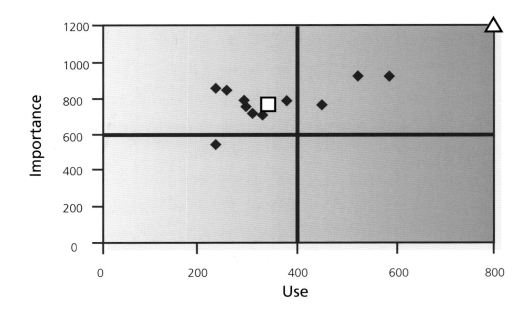

Interpretation

The graph shows a cluster of four companies close to the industry average. Three other pairs of companies are dispersed variously around this point, with one company significantly adrift. We might say that two, possibly three companies, not only consider the use of IT as important, they are also major users. These two or three companies may not have far to travel before they achieve *best practice IT*. The gap between them and the *out-of-sector, best-in-class* company is not so great that it could not be bridged by a concerted effort to invest in more and better IT. The majority of construction companies see the importance of using IT on their sites and do, in fact, use IT to a moderate extent.

Two companies might be described as having a strong commitment to the idea of using IT, but have not made the investment. For one company, the position looks uninspiring. Not only does it fail to use IT to any significant extent, it does not see it as particularly important to the management of construction site processes.

Integration of IT

Brief description

Assessment of the degree of integration of IT for all eleven construction companies relative to one another and best practice.

Results

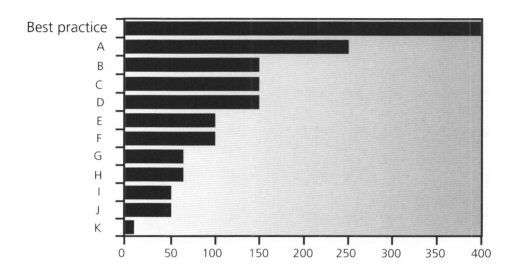

Interpretation

The extent to which the construction companies integrate their IT systems varies dramatically. At one extreme, there is barely any integration. Yet, there is one company which demonstrates a degree of integration that is markedly better than all the others. The gap between it and *best practice IT* is significant, but not so much that it could not be bridged by the same kind of commitment demonstrated by the *out-of-sector, best-in-class* company. It is possible to speculate that the construction company may have reached a critical mass in its implementation and use of IT. Three other construction companies might be described as being on the right path, but with some way to go before they could lay

claim to demonstrating an integrated approach. The remainder appear to have much to do before reaching any degree of systems' integration.

Supporting Statements

Comments by and on the construction companies in regard to their present and future uses of IT

We could not do without IT. Plans include making integration work across [all] systems, greater use of the Internet, procurement tracking (important internationally), time attendance and allocation systems, more use of electronic means for data capture, security control and CCTV.

The company uses IT on site to give people more access to more information:

retrieval and preparation of information is speeded up. The company has plans for the total integration of systems and has one system which integrates accounting, procurement and commercial management. It also plans to change the type of information produced. Asking questions such as: is it correct?, is felt to be the way ahead for successful systems' implementation. The company intends pushing IT to the production work-face with the use of portable PCs and [digital] mobile telephone connections. Video technology, via microwave links, is also contemplated.

Construction is a communications' business. Tools are required for collaborative working so that remote experts can be brought close to the site and so that the site can be close to the experts. Desktop conferencing will be a key technology, with or without video. Digitised still and [full] motion video of site/fabrication shops will be important for remote/virtual meetings. Building modelling using 3-D object modelling forms part of the company's plans.

By sharing data electronically, we have helped to reduce the distance between head office and site. The company operates a policy where the project manager can work from head office for 2-3 days per week whilst still exercising effective project control. The project manager is responsible for the design and construction with an empowered multi-discipline team. Empowerment has allowed the team to choose and experiment with software and systems when they see fit. The company uses a 3-D CAD modelling system as a central production tool in support of site activities. In the future the company will adopt systems for document management, video conferencing, electronic timesheets and procurement and will address issues of integration.

IT is used for commercial advantage to improve quality while making the best use of technology within cost parameters. Plans include integrating and developing systems which eliminate duplication of effort and which use information more effectively. Global site systems are envisaged with electronic links to head office.

IT is a useful tool in the construction process with one caveat – it should never be allowed to take over from face-to-face communication. We often do not appreciate how far we have come in the construction industry with IT take-up within such a short space of time. Plans include electronic systems for managing information in its fullest sense, that is scanning, logging and distributing it. Drawings will be transferred electronically and measurements on site will be captured electronically and down-loaded back in the office. More sophisticated reporting will be adopted so that clients can get the up-to-the minute information they are seeking. Tracking of construction information will form part of this approach.

Recognition of the potential and a desire to develop the use of IT summarises the company's attitude. Plans include the development of an intranet to hold company-wide data and information on health and safety, COSHH and British Standards.

IT enables people to concentrate on core activities, getting rid of mundane work. Management has recognised the need for IT on site and that older members of staff can be trained in its effective use. Plans include extensive use of electronic data exchange, via modems, to handle cost reporting between site and head office, copies of correspondence, accounts, estimating and planning. A procurement system is under development.

The company sums up its use of IT on site as basic and/or heavy domestic rather than light industrial. It considers that smaller sites can benefit more than larger sites from the capabilities of IT in remote [project] management.

The use of IT on site enables everyone to have accurate information access and reporting capabilities on a day-to-day basis. At some point a procurement system will be on-line from head office. There is concern, however, that software written in-house is not accompanied by manuals and training. This tends to be followed by problems once the system(s) are on site. The overall effect is to inhibit the take-up of IT within the company.

The company sums up its use of IT in construction site processes as developing and in need of management and planning.

Comments by and on the engineering-construction company

The company has developed an integrated approach to the management of construction site processes. This is based upon a suite of over 300 automation tools, otherwise known as standard application programs or modules. The objectives of this integration are to:

1. reduce total installed costs;

2. shorten project programmes; and

3. support globalisation by establishing electronic data linkages that will bring together office, sites, customers and suppliers irrespective of their physical location.

The main functions of this integrated systems' approach are to:

- provide services and IT tools that automate and integrate project work processes, including concept design and estimating, detail design, materials' management, construction and project management;

- increase productivity on projects by reducing the time spent on repetitive tasks, reducing or eliminating redundant data entry and increasing accessibility to data required for different processes;

- provide current information such that decision-makers can see data from multiple sources within a single context; and

- include provisions for EDI (electronic data interchange) with customers and suppliers and linkages to third party software.

Process 1: Strategy, policy and procedures

Brief description

Extent to which companies have recognised the need for, and apply, a strategy, policies and procedures for the management of construction site processes, including the use of IT.

Results

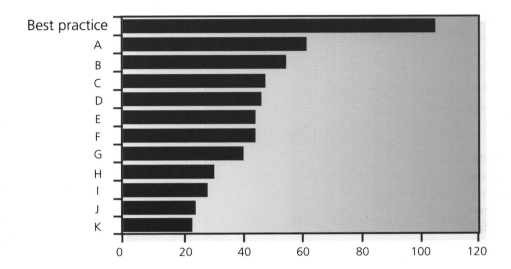

Interpretation

All construction companies have, at least, some kind of formalised approach to dealing with IT in managing construction site processes. Roughly two-thirds of the companies appear to be heading in the right direction, having established procedures. A minority of companies do not, however, appear to have advanced very far in adopting a structured approach to the use of IT in this area of their business. When compared with *best practice IT* even the leading construction companies have some distance to travel before they could regard themselves as having a highly formalised approach to the use of IT. We can also see that the gap between the leading construction company and the *out-of-sector, best-in-class* company is almost the same as that between the leading construction company and the poorest performers in the group.

Comments by the construction companies

IT is used because it improves the efficiency of day-to-day operations and provides the platform for enabling better processes and relationships to come about. ISDN is seen as an essential technology and one that every supplier – taken in the broadest sense – must have. The company does not measure operational benefits arising from IT, as it is regarded as a component of the communications' infrastructure. Cost savings from a reduced amount of reprographics and distribution of information are seen as tangible benefits from the use of IT. The company does not have a formal, written strategy – there is nothing between corporate *feel good* statements and QA procedures. It is, however, corporate policy to use IT on all projects and that they should be networked and linked to head office. On site, there is a total commitment to IT. The company believes that it has vision and that clients generally respond well to this factor. Project teams have considerable autonomy for their management of construction site processes, though IT support is far more structured. All site personnel have routine access to IT and do use it.

Benefits to the business from the use of IT are seen in terms of an ability to keep staffing levels competitive. Other benefits include speeding up information exchange between sites and head office and improving accuracy and timeliness of information reporting. Generally, the benefits of using IT are widely known, though not costed. The exception is when a new system is being considered: resources are then costed. The company has a policy always to use IT on site, but selection of systems is site-dependent. Sometimes clients will insist on a particular selection of IT which can involve retraining. In these cases, experiences have tended to be positive, except that the company has had to bear the cost of purchasing new systems. From an IT perspective, systems are integrated to some extent, with the sharing of data by users from a common database. ISDN lines are used in addition to a leased line for exchanging information with a document control contractor. All site personnel have routine access to IT and almost all use it.

The company does not see the use of IT on site as delivering business benefits, as it sells its service on engineering excellence. Operational benefits from the use of IT are seen, however, in terms of enabling production staff to use information to focus on outputs. This is quite distinct from seeing changes in productivity or quality at the work-face. The use of IT on site is not governed by any formalised approach at this time. Policy statements will, however, be developed. IT has been deployed on construction project sites since it became widely available at an acceptable cost. Even so, project size and staff needs are important considerations when assessing IT investment. Sometimes, a major project office will run a smaller site nearby and share the IT systems.

The company's commitment to IT is recognised by clients whom it has found receptive to its ideas. Construction project sites are autonomous, but derive IT support from head office. This is driven by a central IT department with a person nominated on site to take responsibility for back-ups of data etc.. Someone from the central IT department will be a regular visitor. Not all site personnel have routine access to IT nor can they use it. There are not enough PCs on site for all those who might want to use them. A significant number of staff have missed training and so the level of IT skill is not as high as it might be.

The company sees business benefits arising from serving the customer's needs. In this case, the project is a partnering pilot and the use of IT goes much further than managing construction site processes. The use of IT, in particular a CAD system, supports remote working by the project manager. The control of changes is more effective and IT is used more than ever before. That said, the benefits are difficult to measure. Even so, there is a perception amongst members of the project team that benefits accrue from better control and communication. Whilst construction site processes are quality assured, there is no formal statement of the company's use of IT on site. There is, however, an unwritten, but explicit, policy for site management and IT staff to discuss IT needs at the start of a project. As a rule, IT is deployed on every site, though project size, distance from head office and client attitude are important factors in determining the level of IT. Investment in IT is aligned to financial and corporate strategy. There is a strategic move toward integration to bring members of the design and construction team closer together. Team-working has increased pressure to use IT and empowerment has enabled teams to influence IT investment. Clients influence the extent of IT use on site according to their requirements in reporting and communication of information. A centralised IT function provides support to sites where virtually all personnel have routine access to IT and do, in fact, use it. ISDN is becoming significant for data exchange.

Doing more with less people, cost efficiency and construction process efficiency are seen as benefits for the business from the use of IT on construction project sites. Business and operational benefits are generally not measured. IT investment is based upon knowledge of efficiency and IT initiatives would not occur if cost–benefit analysis were a justification. Faith in the technology is essential. There is, perhaps, one tangible benefit and that is a reduction in the number of secretaries required on the project. This has resulted in a saving in the order of £50,000. The company operates QA-based systems and has a policy statement on project management. It does not, however, have an explicit policy or statement on the use of IT on site. For the development of IT-based systems, the company does have policies for hardware and software choice. The decision to use IT on site is based mostly on function, although size is an important influence. The client can be very influential, especially when dependent upon IT for their own business. Benefits from adopting a particular use of IT include the creation of a project database for helping the client to monitor and control the performance of the building. E-mail has also been used, largely upon the insistence of the client.

Whilst the project site is autonomous, links to the head office exist for e-mail and accounting and procurement functions. All site personnel can and do use IT routinely.

Managers are able to have information to enable them to manage effectively rather than their wasting time on mundane tasks that IT can automate. Cost cutting helps the company retain a competitive edge for survival in the market-place. Other benefits from IT are from the monitoring of site activities. It is used primarily to monitor financial performance which is a measure of efficiency. IT also improves management information and can be used as a tool for learning. Benefits are not measured. Any assessment is based on *gut feeling*. The company operates a QA system which defines group policy and site operations and procedures. There is also a management guide covering the buying, management and cost control. Most sites have PCs, the main determinants are staff, size of project and specific requirements. There has been some experience of clients demanding a particular use of IT. The results have not been especially beneficial and there is the feeling that clients sometimes do not have the capacity or capability themselves to handle what they have imposed. The site has autonomy, though some head office services are used. Most systems are separate from the head office, with the responsibility for IT vested in the site and backed-up with support from the central IT function in head office. Most site personnel can and do use IT. ISDN is used for linking regional offices, but not sites.

Competitive advantage is achieved through the use of IT on site. Operational efficiency of site activities is improved as is communication, presentation, costing and management. These benefits are not, however, quantified and are more likely to be based on *gut feeling* stemming from noticeable improvements in working practices. The company has devised metrics for analysing the performance of its document management systems. Management of construction site processes is based on procedures found in the company's QA manual. In terms of IT, there is no explicit policy or statement on its use. The deployment of IT on sites has been evolutionary. The only system the site could not manage without is that for accounting. Virtually all sites have IT, although the contract sum determines the IT budget [for the site]. Clients have intervened in the choice of project planning and valuation systems. This has been welcomed when the client wants also to use the company's systems as this can lead to more effective sharing of information. Client intervention is unwelcome when an unfamiliar package is pushed on to the company. More than 80% of the company's sites have autonomy in terms of management. Sites have autonomy to deploy IT in support of operational procedures. Financial [commercial] management is integrated with head office. A support manager is appointed for dealing with hardware; the rest is down to individuals. Almost all professional, technical and managerial staff have routine access to IT and do make use of it. ISDN is used to link the site to head office, with megastream lines between the four individual site offices.

IT is planned and used at the operational level, although a system has been developed and used to promote the business as an innovator in the development of software. The company recognises that there is quicker production of information which is also better controlled and more consistent. The benefits of IT are self-evident from the [reduced] staffing levels on site. There are felt to be some very real benefits from IT use on site, for example the time taken for the production of a valuation has reduced from three days to one day from the use of networked PCs used by the

site-based QSs. The company has a QA led system, with many documents stored electronically. Monthly progress reports are automatically produced with the assistance of proprietary software. IT investment is a site-based choice that attracts backing from head office. A committee has been charged with the responsibility of drawing up an IT policy for the company. The actual level of IT investment on site is related to staffing levels with the cost of IT allowed for in the bid for the project. The site is autonomous in terms of its management, although reporting to head office – using hard copy – is undertaken monthly. A member of the head office staff – an IT specialist – is responsible for site-based systems. Virtually all personnel have routine access to IT and do, in fact, use it. However, physical constraints of site work make it difficult to use IT solutions without constant return trips to site offices.

IT improvements are predominantly focused on operational issues. Benefits are not quantified. The company has QA systems, although this does not extend to IT. If the decision is taken to use IT, there are company guidelines on the choice of hardware or software. Choice depends upon staff levels, type of project management and the availability of hardware from other sites. Sharing of programme information with the client, via disks, takes place. An ISDN line was installed, but later removed after lack of company support. The project manager has autonomy for the site and a monthly review takes place between the site and head office. The project manager and IT department are jointly responsible for IT policy and use. Whilst all site personnel have access to IT, the level of use by non-secretarial/clerical staff is low. A lack of equipment and appropriate skills are blamed for this situation.

IT is expected to provide better information about site activities to enable management to take corrective action if required. IT is also expected to reduce administrative costs. A project planning system is used to enable quick evaluations of the project's status to be produced and deficient areas to be highlighted. The frequency of reporting on projects has increased from monthly to weekly intervals. This has improved the level of knowledge about the project. Management of construction site processes is covered by QA procedures. Detailed procedures are used to guide IT acquisition for sites. The amount of IT to be used on site is based on the merits of the project, but size and staffing levels are important factors. All sites that have a secretary have a PC. Clients intervene seldom in the use of IT on site. The site has autonomy unless major decisions or budget deviations are made. There is a close relationship with head office. Planning, engineering and QS functions are managed separately away from head office. Accounting and administration are integrated with head office. The company's central IT department is responsible for site-based IT. Little more than one third of non-secretarial/clerical personnel have routine access to IT and use it. A lack of equipment is blamed, as well as the inappropriateness of some work.

Business decisions are made at head office and do not make it clear if IT use on site is expected to deliver benefits to the business. Operational benefits are seen in terms of faster access to information, control over documents received and sent and [support for] programming. Benefits are not measured, rather they are based on gut feeling and a knowledge that operations are more efficient with IT assistance. The company operates QA procedures. There is a lack of recognition of the need for IT for the main board although an IT policy document does exist.

The need for, and use of, IT is a site-based choice. The site is autonomous with weekly reporting to head office. IT systems are separated from head office functions, although some access to head office systems, via modem, occurs. No specific person is designated responsible for site-based IT systems. The QS department is generally responsible for IT. All site personnel can use IT, yet those who do are few. A lack of education is blamed along with a shortage (or lack) of computers. Despite this situation, no one has pushed for more computers.

Authors' comment. Confusion between a strategy and procedures is apparent in a number of cases. This tends to suggest that IT is seen as important at the operational level, but not necessarily as something of strategic importance to the business. This was also a finding of the study of IT in supplier management, where questions aimed at assessing the strategic importance of IT were confused with matters of procedure.

Comments on the engineering-construction company

The company's integrated approach to construction project management focuses on five key phases: optimisation, engineering, procurement, construction and project management. Significant in the development of this approach is the adoption of open standards and communication protocols. Presently, the company's strategy is to migrate all its systems to a *Windows 95/NT* environment in which servers and clients communicate via a uniform data bus (or information layer exchange) using the TCP/IP standard. Both local area networks and wide area networks have adopted TCP/IP as the primary means for integrating a global topology. In-house developed software and third party products, typically relational database management and project planning and scheduling software, are integrated alongside popular office automation tools. In this way, the company has pushed hard for uniformity in technology order to achieve a high level of conformity in its work practices.

Process 2: Management, supervision and administration

Brief description

Extent to which companies attach importance, and apply IT, to management, supervision and administration of sites.

Results

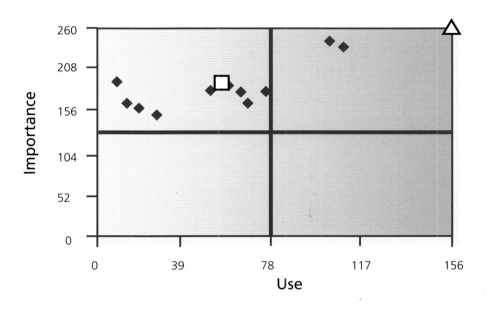

Interpretation

All construction companies recognise the importance of IT in managing, supervising and administering their sites, but only two companies use IT to a significant extent. The latter can be clearly differentiated from the remaining nine companies by their distance from the main cluster and the industry average. They are also markedly close to achieving *best practice IT* than any of the remainder. One company appears to be highly committed to the idea of using IT, yet has the lowest level of actual use of all companies. Overall, the distance between the best and the worst performers is considerable.

Comments by and on the construction companies

A document management system is used extensively to support many activities within this process. Spreadsheets, e-mail and swipe card systems are also used. The company sees the benefits of IT in the speed of collation of information, the ability to interrogate databases for checking document status, overall accuracy and accessibility by a number of users. Disbenefits of IT in this context are seen in the requirement for more training and a reliance upon electronic information. It is also suspected that people will ask for information that they do not really need.

The company makes extensive use of IT to support this process. A document management system is used for storing and retrieving information including correspondence, minutes, progress reports, instructions, drawing register and other technical functions. The DMS automatically checks for responses and prompts when action is required. The system also has application in the area of claims' resolution. Scanning is used for capturing information. Generally, the company sees significant benefits from the system and no disbenefits except that a learning curve is involved.

Electronic communication plays a significant part in the IT used to support this process. E-mail runs in parallel with paper-based systems for correspondence, instructions and the like. Database management is used for some applications. The company is enthusiastic about electronic data exchange, but is concerned about the legal aspects. Hard copy is still produced and used for several activities. Speed of reaction and an increase in operating efficiency are seen as the main benefits from IT use. There is a feeling that IT also raises the company's profile.

An integrated system has been developed by the company to bring together various facets of this and other processes. RFIs, instructions, progress reports, notices and a drawing register are all supported in this way. Correspondence is not scanned as it is seen as difficult to justify economically. That apart, other activities are supported by at least word processing and so the vast majority of information is held electronically. Benefits are in speed of access and retrieval of information, presentation quality and ensuring a consistent approach. One problem is that there is a need to train people to understand information as an entity and to understand how electronic filing, storage etc. can and does work.

The company uses a variety of technology to support the activities within this process. These include a document management system and database management system for handling instructions, progress reports and correspondence. Benefits of using IT here are seen in cost reduction, speed of distribution [of information], retrieval and access. IT use is progressing at a rate that is difficult to match technically. That is, the nature of the applications have not changed very much over the years: practices are evolutionary, not revolutionary.

Database management and word processing combine to support a number of activities. Out-going correspondence, minutes, instructions, progress reports, notices and a drawing register are accommodated by the database which is supplemented by the use of word processing. Benefits for site management are seen as ease of information retrieval and access. In terms of disbenefits, reliability of hardware is called into question along with mismatch of some software for the purpose it was intended. Dependence upon IT for access to information is also a worry. The educational level of operatives is getting lower and lower and this will make the take-up of IT at the work-face difficult.

Database management and word processing are used to support a number of activities in this process area. Instructions and drawings are logged in a database and word processing software is used to help keep track of individual documents needed to support claims. IT is seen to increase the speed of operations, access to information, accuracy, consistency and presentation quality. Lack of education leads to a degree of restricted use of IT.

Spreadsheets and word processing support several of the activities within this process area. E-mail is used to transmit the output of some activities, for example RFIs and requests for technical information.

Otherwise, the remainder of the activities are paper-based. IT is seen as having benefits for site management in speed and accessibility of information.

IT is used to support a number of activities, most of which is word processing. Speed, clarity and presentation quality are seen as the main benefits for site management and other parties closely associated with the project.

Few activities within this process area are supported by IT, except to note that word processing is used for correspondence, minutes, progress reports and notices. A modem connection to head office is, however, used to transmit allocation sheets. Where used, IT has benefits in saving time, increasing availability of information and speed of access to it. Software is still in the development stage and unreliable. The entire system once crashed and locked out everyone.

Apart from the use of word processors for supporting correspondence, minutes, progress reports and notices, everything else is paper-based. Despite this, benefits from the use of IT are seen in terms of savings in manpower and in the retrieval of information.

Comments by and on the engineering-construction company

Several integrated software modules support the management of the site. Contract administration leans heavily on automated tools and these are linked in turn to project planning and scheduling. Document management is central to this process and the company has developed an electronic information management system. An on-line reference library contains current standards, procedures, design guides, lessons learned and best practices that underpin other application-specific areas. Another system contains historical data that can be applied and customised for individual projects.

The document management system controls and tracks all project documents, including those from the client and suppliers. These systems allow integrated electronic access for controlling, creating, viewing, editing, red-lining, archiving and handling all project documents.

Process 3: Commercial management

Brief description

Extent to which companies attach importance, and apply IT, to the commercial management of sites.

Results

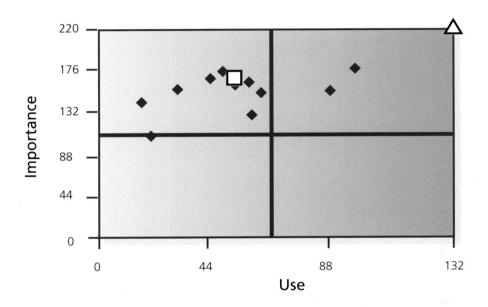

Interpretation

All companies, with one possible exception, see the use of IT as important. The pattern is similar to that for managing, supervising and administering sites, with two companies strongly committed to the use of IT as well as recognising its underlying importance. Three companies might be regarded as using IT to a limited extent and one of these presumably does not see this as a problem. The gap between the two leading construction companies and *best practice IT* is not great. Overall, the distance between the best and the worst performers is once again considerable.

Comments by and on the construction companies

The company has developed its own integrated solution as an implementation of a relational database management system. It covers the entire process of commercial management in its role as a professional manager. Benefits arise from simply having all the data in one place and accessible to those who need it. In this respect, it is important for everyone to realise that other people will probably want to use the data so it has to be correct and be communicable.

A system for managing valuations, variations and final accounts is used. This is complemented by a document management system and spreadsheet applications. Payments are automated to the extent that cheques are generated from a sub-contractor ledger. The company sees benefits arising from the speed of operations, savings in manpower and increases in efficiency leading to more effective business management. Reliance on the systems is such that problems would arise if there were some kind of failure.

A combination of IT solutions is used to automate activities in this process. These include a database management system, the document management system and spreadsheets for which many applications are noted. Benefits for the company include speed and accuracy, *what if?* scenarios, ready access to information and the ability to make changes to both data and report generation features. The latter factor is, however, also considered to be a specific disbenefit.

Virtually all activities within this process area are supported by IT, mostly in the form of spreadsheets. The exceptions are the capturing and maintenance of daywork sheets and where a pro-forma is used for sending information to head office with respect to sub-contract payments. Greater clarity, time-saving, presentation quality, error-correction and reliability are cited as the benefits from using IT. Concerns exist, however, over the total use of IT, as this can remove the *feel* which surveyors, in particular, have over certain cost data.

Most activities rely on the use of spreadsheets, although bills of quantities are handled by a proprietary software package. Some transfer of output via disk and e-mail is undertaken, typically in variations, final accounts and cash flow forecasting. Accessibility of information and accuracy are cited as the main benefits for site management and other key parties.

Database management is used to support variations and bills of quantities work, with

spreadsheets for most other activities. The company takes the view that they could not do without IT, though recognise the lack of sufficient software modules to integrate the process.

The company uses an estimating and valuations' system to cover many of the otherwise discrete activities within this process area. This is supplemented by the use of a database management system and spreadsheets. Benefits are related to cost reductions and increased speed with which activities can be undertaken.

Spreadsheets are used to a significant extent, especially for dealing with valuations, variations, dayworks, final accounts and cash flow. The company sees benefits for site management from this use of IT in terms of improved quality of information, time savings, flexibility, accuracy, consistency and the opportunity to generate *what if?* scenarios. On the down side, the time needed for staff to become proficient in the use of software can cause problems when project timescales are tight.

A valuation system is used to support the preparation of final accounts. For other activities, significant use is made of spreadsheets and some e-mailing of outputs occurs in the area of sub-contract accounts, variations and dayworks. The company sees improved control over the process as a distinct benefit of using IT. Limitations in the use of IT are caused, it is believed, by personal ambitions and aspirations not being high enough. Some degree of experimentation is taking place.

Significant use is made of spreadsheets for handling sub-contract accounts, variations, dayworks and cash flow forecasts. Modem connections provide the means for exchanging data with head office. There are widespread benefits from the use of IT.

Spreadsheets are used for supporting most activities and are seen to have benefits in increased speed and accuracy. All output is paper-based. The need to train people to use systems and the testing of software during a project can be a worrying business.

Comments by and on the engineering-construction company

Various software modules are co-ordinated to provide support for estimating, budgetary control, labour productivity and cost performance, contract commitments and payments. Commercial management is much more broadly defined and deals with a degree of complexity that is generally absent from building and civil engineering projects. Also, the process is not quite so separately identifiable, as it is in the UK, being integrated with other project management applications such as programme reporting and contract administration. Even so, commercial management concentrates upon knowing exactly what the financial status is of any part of the project at any time. The single database concept ensures that, unlike its construction company counterparts, re-keying of data is unnecessary. This is also a function of the strong vertical and horizontal integration that exists between processes and activities.

Process 4: Legal, health and safety

Brief description

Extent to which companies attach importance to the use of IT for the management of legal, health and safety requirements on sites.

Results

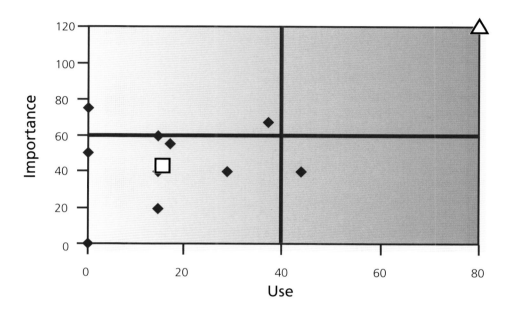

Interpretation

Most construction companies have a low level of commitment to the use of IT and, more worrying, see IT as unimportant in supporting this process. One company regards IT as quite important and is reasonably committed to using IT; another uses more IT despite attaching lower importance to its use. A further company was not able to respond to questions on either use or importance of IT and two companies use no IT though do recognise its importance. The gap between the construction companies and *best practice IT* is significant.

Comments by and on the construction companies

Building regulations, British Standards and Codes of Practice are available on CD-ROM. Additionally, a database management system is used to handle information on CDM regulations. Safety policies and information on COSHH are word processed. Apart from the obvious benefits of accuracy, accessibility and consistency of information, IT helps to provide an effective audit trail. This is especially important in the case of CDM.

The company relies on a mix of database management and document management to support aspects of this process, particularly COSHH, CDM and training. Other activities are word processed and/or

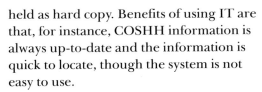

held as hard copy. Benefits of using IT are that, for instance, COSHH information is always up-to-date and the information is quick to locate, though the system is not easy to use.

A database management system is used for handling information on COSHH, CDM and British Standards. The primary benefit of IT for this process is to make information more accessible for site management.

Whilst most of the activities are paper-based, a database management system is used to handle information and requirements with respect to COSHH and CDM regulations. Word processed safety policy documents are issued. The benefit of IT is mainly in providing ready access to information for site management.

Apart from a swipe card system for controlling site security, IT is absent from the other activities within this process. The company feels that IT has limited potential, except for site security work.

A safety management system is used to report incidents and cover security and checking-in. IT is not, however, considered so relevant in this context as data captured here cannot be used much elsewhere. Other activities in this process area are not supported by IT.

The company uses a proprietary software package for handling COSHH matters. The package is written as an application of a low cost database management system. Legal, health and safety information in an electronic form would make information retrieval easier. Problems are seen in the electronic accessing of copyrighted material such as British Standards and Codes of Practice.

Safety records have to be kept for all current and past employees. This is done without the particular use of IT.

IT is not used at all in this process area.

Comments by and on the engineering-construction company

The nature of the work undertaken by the company means that it is brought into far greater contact with project circumstances that demand the highest health and safety standards. Working on an existing plant or nuclear facility means that safety is paramount. For these reasons, the company has well established procedures backed by IT. Again, the theme is one of integration with other applications such that information can be accessed rapidly. Health and safety data include health records of the work-force, safety inspection records, causal analysis stemming from accidents where these have occurred and statutory reporting.

Process 5: Planning, monitoring and control

Brief description

Extent to which companies attach importance and apply IT to the planning, monitoring and control of site activities.

Results

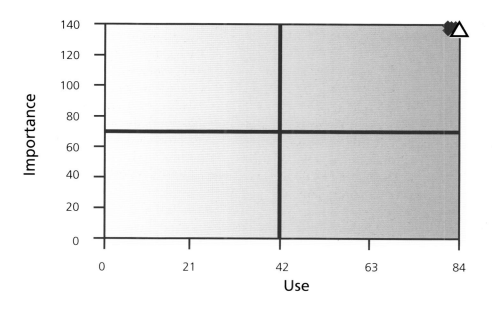

Interpretation

All construction companies not only see IT as important in supporting this process, they all use it. For these reasons, the performance of all eleven companies matches *best practice IT.* That said, the extent to which companies use IT – each has a project planning and scheduling system – various enormously. The weakness in this particular benchmark is that it is not sufficiently sensitive to the degree to which companies use their systems dynamically in anticipating events as opposed merely to reacting to them. Further study of this process is needed to provide better answers.

Comments by and on the construction companies

A proprietary software package is used, one that is based on network analysis and which produces Gantt charts. Progress can be recorded and delays monitored, as well as testing possible scenarios. Benefits to the company are seen in terms of the ability to identify problem areas quickly and interrogation of the database. On the down side, the package can be difficult to use and there are too few skilled users.

Two project planning and scheduling systems are used. The systems are used for monitoring progress, resource levelling, *what if?* scenario building and for determining the consequences of a delay. Speed of operation is seen as the main benefit, though this can be adversely affected if the client's consultants are not using IT. Specialist expertise is needed to drive the systems.

A fully networked planning and scheduling system is used. This is used to programme all tasks including those undertaken off-site. Productivity monitoring is used to determine the end value of each works package. *What if?* analysis is undertaken routinely, along with forecasting. Other benefits are that the system is user friendly and effective at trend analysis. On the down side, too few people use the system and even when they do it can take a lot of effort.

Three different project planning and scheduling systems are used by the company. The decision to use which particular system depends on the circumstances of the project. Links to an integrated system for commercial and other management processes are provided. The company sees project planning systems as production management tools. They are not provided to generate productivity data.

The company has developed its own project planning and scheduling system which covers, *inter alia*, network analysis, Gantt charting, resource levelling, as-built planning and time-chainage reporting. Links to a system for valuations and financial reporting are provided. The planning and scheduling system relies on manual entry of data, although all subsequent manipulation of data is done electronically. The system is considered essential. Benefits to the company are in enabling effective planning to take place.

The company uses a proprietary software package for critical path analysis, generation of Gantt charts, monitoring or progress, production of as-built programmes and *what if?* analyses. It sees this as essential for speed, consistency and flexibility. The main beneficiaries are site management. A worrying disbenefit from the use of IT is that some members of staff do not have much faith in the results produced by the software.

A project planning and scheduling package is used to produce the initial programme for the project and for subsequent monitoring of progress. Barcharts can be generated and *what if?* scenarios can be tested. The package is also used to estimate contract delays due to client-inspired changes.

Planning, resource control and monitoring are supported by a proprietary software package. Cash flow forecasting and monitoring is also covered. Generally, the package is typical of those used for project planning and scheduling. Specific benefits are seen in terms of ease of manipulation of data, speed, accuracy and reliability. A disbenefit of using IT in this context is that the entire team requires training.

A project planning and scheduling system is used by the company to support a range of activities that are not dissimilar to those of other companies. *What if?* scenarios are generated with dynamic planning over time. One draw back is that the package is difficult for the inexperienced user. Some difficulties with programme logic have become apparent. The software may be expensive, but is felt to be worth it.

A proprietary project planning and scheduling system is used by the company to undertake critical path analysis, produce Gantt charts, report on progress and generate *what if?* scenarios. The benefits are in better manipulation of information, speed and presentation of information. The system also has the ability to deal with complexity which is difficult for managers, but successful use relies on competent staff.

The company uses a popular project planning and scheduling system which covers progress monitoring, reporting, *what if?* analysis and risk assessment. The benefits of IT are that a turnkey solution can be used to provide an integrated approach to project management. There are concerns, however, that when all the planning has been completed, there is the chance that the user may forget the physical aspect of the work and, instead, concentrate on the abstract computer model.

Comments by and on the engineering-construction company

Two software modules are used within the company and are of the same kind as used in several of the construction companies. However, they are an integral part of the software infrastructure for the engineering-construction company. Features also include resource allocation and resource levelling. Apart from planning and scheduling functions, the company undertakes a good deal of performance measurement. It monitors and reports on programme and cost performance by extracting and compiling necessary information from other modules within the total system; for example, CPM processors and corporate financial systems. Engineering performance is also measured in terms of budgets and progress against programme; additionally, the system can support personnel planning. An important interface is that to a 3-D modelling system to enable construction to be simulated and schedules to be defined. A walkthrough facility allows construction personnel to plan work schedules on a more realistic basis and to suggest corrective action to a design where buildability issues are brought into question.

Process 6: Delivery and materials' handling

Brief description

Extent to which companies attach importance and apply IT in managing deliveries and materials' handling on sites.

Results

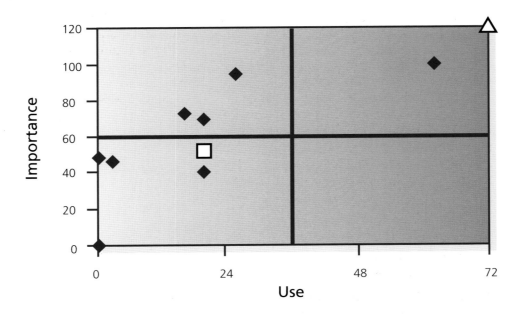

Interpretation

There is considerable variation in performance in regard to the use of IT. In two cases, the construction companies see IT as very important and use it to a significant extent. For most companies, however, the use of IT is of a low order and is not seen as important. In three cases, the companies did not respond. Most companies would appear, on the face of it, not to see this process as particularly important. For two companies – as we have noted – the gap between their performance and *best practice IT* is relatively small. This process has links to *supplier management* which was the theme of the first benchmarking study.

Comments by and on the construction companies

A materials' reconciliation system is used which covers requisitions, purchase orders, material call-off and GRNs. Benefits are seen in faster information storage and retrieval, that is better access to information, although time for keying in data can be significant.

The company has its own purchase order control system. This follows the process from requisition to the raising of purchase orders. A system for automatic ordering, handling of GRNs and invoice matching is being piloted. The main benefits of IT in this context are seen in terms of not paying suppliers twice, saving time and reducing transaction costs. A specific concern is the

entry of information into the system.

The company has a system which deals with a number of activities within this process area. GRNs and plant returns fall within the use of the system. Purchase orders are generated and handled by computer as is inventory control. Accessibility, accuracy and an auditable trail of transactions between the company and its suppliers are seen as the main benefits of IT.

Database management is used for handling purchase orders. Material call off for selected building elements is supported by CAD. Elsewhere, word processing of plant returns takes place. IT is seen to offer efficiency gains and benefits to all involved. There are no specific disbenefits from using IT to support this process area.

All activities are paper-based within this process area. IT is not used. Plant returns are singled out for potential support by IT as this might improve cost control.

Apart from the use of the company's accounting system for handling GRNs and plant returns, no other IT is used in this process area.

Spreadsheets are used for handling material call off, GRNs and plant returns, otherwise the remainder of activities are paper-based. Timeliness and speed of operation are the main benefits from using IT. Some requisitions are, by necessity, manually-based transactions.

Word processing is used to support the production of plant returns. Other activities are paper-based. Suppliers cannot handle electronic information.

Comments by and on the engineering-construction company

A procurement tracking system, based on a multi-user database, covers: material control, supplier information, purchasing, expediting and inspection, traffic and logistics and inventory control. The company claims dramatic gains from the widespread use of IT in this area. Excess inventory has been reduced to a tiny percentage – as low as 1.4% on one project – and processing time for material receiving reports (GRNs) has been reduced from two and a half days to less than 24 hours. The system ensures that the correct materials are ordered, fabricated and delivered on schedule at the best price. It monitors the status of materials, from initial identification to delivery, and is a paper-less process. Bar coding and portable data terminal technology are employed.

Process 7: Production on site and off site

Brief description

Extent to which companies attach importance and apply IT in managing production on and off site.

Results

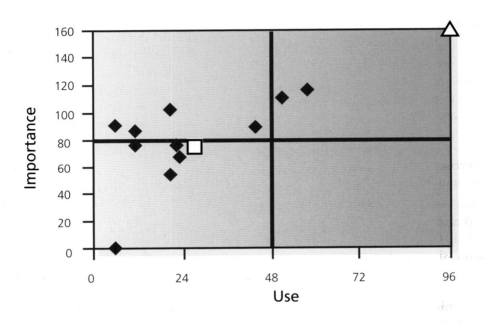

Interpretation

The pattern of use and importance of IT reflected by the construction companies is again widely dispersed and is similar to the results for other processes. One company uses hardly any IT and does not see it as important; another likewise uses very little IT, although does see it as important. Most companies appear to regard IT as at least moderately important and two, possibly three, have made a real commitment to using IT. Even so, there is a significant gap between the performance of the leading construction companies and *best practice IT.*

Comments by and on the construction companies

This process relies heavily on IT. A document management system supports drawing, specification and contract information. Other activities are supported to varying degrees by IT. The company sees benefits to site management through faster processing and accessibility of information. There are no specific disbenefits.

CAD is used to handle drawings and to assist in setting out. Exchange of drawing files (in DXF format) takes place. Laser technology is used in measuring on site. For other activities, word processing is used to generate and maintain information in electronic form. Benefits of IT use include speed, accuracy, accessibility, reliability and, in the case of CAD, clash detection and consistency checking.

An integrated systems' approach is taken to supporting activities in this process area. Quality plans and reports, along with drawing files are handled by the system. For other activities, word processing is considered appropriate.

Use is made of spreadsheets to support measurement and the production of QA plans and reports. EDM technology is also used to aid measurement and disk-based data are used for setting out. Benefits for setting out are in speed and accuracy. Some people see QA as a paper-generating exercise where the use of IT can increase the amount of paper dramatically.

The company exchanges drawing files on disk and specifications are received by e-mail. Other activities make use of word processing, typically for quality plans, reports and maintenance records. IT is seen to provide benefits in terms of a convenient and rapid storage and retrieval function. A specific disbenefit of IT is that people do not always know or bother enough about the information they are accessing and exchanging electronically.

This process is supported by a limited amount of IT. Word processing of QA documents and spreadsheets for measurement are indicative of the extent of application. Satellite technology (GPS) is, however, used for setting out purposes. Problems of applying IT in this process area are seen in terms of the need for specialist skills and training.

Quality plans and reports are stored in the company's document management system and manipulated by word processor. Apart from that and the use of electronic surveying equipment for setting out, there is no other use of IT in this area.

With the exception of measurement, which uses EDM technology, no other activities are supported by IT.

All activities, except for setting out, rely on paper-based systems. IT is used only in the context of ground models to assist in setting out.

QA plans and reports are supported by IT in the form of word processing. The remaining activities are all paper-based. Even so, the company sees IT as having a distinct potential benefit in providing greater control over production.

The use of IT is confined to measurement and word processing QA plans and reports. A measurement package is used, but does not comply with the requirements of CESMM.

Comments by and on the engineering-construction company

The company's approach to integration provides it with a focus on how to ensure that production is right first time. The use of computer simulation, as an interesting example of convergence of technology, enables the buildability of a design to be tested before any construction takes place. This particular system is highly interactive and has been used for some years to help in planning project execution, particularly in refurbishing nuclear reactors. The system graphically animates project schedules in the 3-D model for the facility. Temporary facilities are also modelled with checks for interference-free installation and removal paths. Rule-based and manual sequence planning are incorporated. Many software modules are used to manage production and some are also used in training. Examples include a graphical tool for planning and optimising crane positions and operations, inventory control of tools and tool usage, maintenance and operations management.

5. Conclusions

What has been learned from the study?

There is clear evidence of the widespread use of IT in support of construction processes. That said, the range of performance amongst eleven leading construction companies is also wide and, in some cases, well below what might be expected of a modern, competitive industry. The distance between the best performers and the worst is significant, as is the gap between the best and the *out-of-sector, best practice* example. Construction site processes may, in the context of this study, cover myriad applications and issues. In whatever way these are represented, they still constitute what has to be a fundamental part of the business of any construction company.

The picture that emerges is a mixed one. For some companies, integration is a goal which they have set themselves and the evidence would confirm their commitment to this ideal. For others, a struggle to establish a critical mass of IT on their sites is evident. Worse still, a few companies are using IT tools which have not changed in a decade in an attempt to automate traditional paper-based systems. There is little evidence amongst the majority of companies to indicate that they are determined to break with this tradition. Despite having requested that companies nominate their best sites, we cannot help but wonder what the worst might be: presumably, these would simply have no IT. Our intention is not to insult individuals and companies facing difficult times. But to pretend that somehow all is about right, would be to fail those very companies.

Serious efforts have to be made to transform predominantly disparate,
paper-based systems into an integrated whole in the case of two, possibly three, companies. Success will not come overnight and so some serious long term investment is needed. The hidden danger as always in studies of this kind is in comparing one's performance with that of a close competitor. Where the result is close, it may be tempting to conclude that whilst there is room for improvement the problem is not major. Our conclusion would be to stress the opposite.

The introduction of a credible *out-of-sector* comparison has shown that the construction industry is under-performing in its use of IT in managing construction site processes. Useful lessons can be learned from best practice as exemplified by the engineering-construction company. IT is vital to its mission-critical process of construction site management. Without IT, the company would not exist, let alone survive in the marketplace.

Recommendations for effective management of construction site processes

Many lessons can be learned from the findings of this benchmarking study and the *out-of-sector* comparison with engineering-construction. These can be thought of as factors that are critical to the successful implementation and exploitation of IT in support of the management of construction site processes.

● A strategy which elevates the importance of IT in supporting construction site processes is required of all companies and this must include a clear statement of where the company is aiming its sights.

- Construction companies must re-examine the underlying business processes which presently constitute construction site processes and redefine them in a way that will align them to delivering against client and customer objectives.

- Integration has been talked about for decades in the construction industry. Improved electronic exchange of information is required if the benefits of powerful third party software are to be harnessed. In order to achieve this aim, companies must invest in IT infrastructure of the kind that will allow for open communications based on industry standard protocols.

- Training is judged, even by the companies, to be of a low priority and something provided on a need-to-know basis. More could and should be done to educate the work-force – and that means everyone on site – in the use of IT in its many forms.

Recommendations for research and innovation

The benchmarking in this study has measured two factors:

- how important IT is for a particular process; and

- how effectively IT is being used to support that process.

By depicting these two measures within a grid – as shown previously in the six individual comparisons – it is possible to classify a benchmark in the following way.

Important area where IT is poorly used	Effective current use of IT
Non-priority area for IT at present	High, ineffective use of IT

Table 2: Classification of benchmarks

This classification can now be used as a pointer for research and innovation priorities.

Short term research priorities	System development priorities
Possible long term research priorities	Non-priority area

Table 3: Identification of research and innovation priorities

If the results of this benchmarking study are now superimposed on the above, it is possible to categorise overall performance and average performance of the six processes in the following way.

Overall performance. Managing and supervising. Commercial Management.	Planning, monitoring and control.
Legal, health & safety. Deliveries and material handling. Production on and off site.	

Table 4: Priorities in management of construction site processes

The next steps

This study is a snapshot of current practice in IT in construction site processes. Repeating it at some time would reveal where progress had been made and where attention is still required. Benchmarking is, after all, a tool for continuous improvement. Given the evidence presented in this report, there is clearly much improvement to be had.

References and Bibliography

DOE (1995)

Construct IT: Bridging the gap, report and management summary

London, HMSO, *68*

Construct IT provides the framework of an information technology strategy for the UK construction industry. The report highlights the advance of technology, the lessons for the UK construction industry arising from other industries use of IT, the issues, strategy and an outline implementation programme for which the *Construct IT Centre of Excellence* has responsibility for co-ordinating and promoting UK research.

Leibfried, K H J and McNair, C J (1994)

Benchmarking: a tool for continuous improvement

London, Harper Collins Publishers Ltd, *xx + 344*

This is a comprehensive work covering almost an A-Z of the benchmarking process. Whilst written from a US perspective it does, nonetheless, provide a detailed account of the *why?* and *how?* of the subject irrespective of one's location or experiences. There is a wealth of knowledge and expertise embodied in this book, much of it pithy case study material. The book forms part of The Coopers and Lybrand Performance Solutions Series.

Appendix A

List of Members of the Construct IT Centre of Excellence

As at June 1996

Contractors

Alfred McAlpine, AMEC, Balfour Beatty, Bovis, Costain, Kyle Stewart, John Laing, Tarmac, Taylor Woodrow, Tilbury Douglas, Trafalgar House, Wimpey

Consultants

BDP, Bucknall Group, KPMG, WS Atkins

Clients

BAA, Boots, Whitbread

IT industry

Bentley Systems, Engineering Technology, Intergraph, Unisys

Communications

BT, Mercury

Suppliers

Tarmac Building Products

Professional bodies and associations

ACE, BMP, British Cement Association, CIBSE, CIOB, CIRIA, CITE, Construction IT Forum, EDICON, RIBA, The RICS, Steel Construction Institute

Universities and institutes

Loughborough, Nottingham, Reading, Salford, Sheffield, Strathclyde, UCL and BRE

Appendix B

List of issues addressed by the questionnaire

Strategy, policy and procedures

- business and operational benefits of IT
- quantification of business and operational benefits
- explicit statement on management and supervision
- explicit policy or statement on the use of IT on site
- basis of decision to use IT on site
- networking of IT on site
- extent of client intervention in choice of IT
- reaction of company to client stipulation
- benefits delivered to client
- benefits delivered to company
- treatment of sites as separate entities
- treatment of sites as separate entities for use of IT
- alternative action in the event of no IT linkage
- responsibility for site-based IT
- responsibility for technical support/back-up
- policy for dealing with site-based IT at project end
- use of IT in archiving hard copy
- access of site personnel to IT
- use by site personnel of IT
- reasons for non-use of IT
- extent of electronic flows of information between site and elsewhere
- permanent of special communication links

- statement on company's use of IT on site

Management, supervision and administration

- applications of IT covering capture, storage, manipulation and transmission including site diary, correspondence, minutes, RFIs, labour allocation, payroll, progress reports, notices and claims, instructions, drawing register and technical information
- benefits and specific disbenefits of using IT in this process area

Commercial management

- applications of IT covering capture, storage, manipulation and transmission including bills of quantities, estimating, valuations, sub-contracts, variations, dayworks, payments, cost and claims, instructions, drawing register and technical information
- benefits and specific disbenefits of using IT in this process area

Legal, health and safety

- applications of IT covering capture, storage, manipulation and transmission including safety policy, COSHH/CDM regulations, insurance, building regulations, British Standards and Codes of Practice.
- benefits and specific disbenefits of using IT in this process area

Planning, monitoring and control

- applications of IT covering capture, storage, manipulation and transmission including Gantt charts, network analysis, method statement, resource levelling, progress reports and exception reports

- benefits and specific disbenefits of using IT in this process area

Delivery and materials' handling

- applications of IT covering capture, storage, manipulation and transmission including requisitions, purchase orders, materials call off, GRNs and plant returns

- benefits and specific disbenefits of using IT in this process area

Production on-site and off-site

- applications of IT covering capture, storage, manipulation and transmission including QA plans and reports, contract terms, drawings, specification, setting out and measurement

- benefits and specific disbenefits of using IT in this process area

Acknowledgements

The study team is pleased to acknowledge the contributions of the twelve companies that gave permission for the benchmarks to be undertaken and for allowing their staff to participate in this work. Particular appreciation is expressed for members of the steering group who helped to shape the form and content of the study. These are Herbie Boyle, Derek Blundell, David Leonard, Steve Marshall and Barry Powley.

Table of contents

Executive Summary

1. Eleven construction companies took part in the benchmarking of IT use in construction site processes. The eleven are amongst the leading construction companies in the UK.

2. The scope of IT use in construction site processes is diverse and covers: managing, supervising and administering; commercial management; legal, health and safety; planning, monitoring and control; delivery and materials' handling; and production on and off site. Strategy, policy and procedures also fall within this scope.

3. Each company was asked to nominate its best construction project site from the perspective of IT use. These sites were visited and personnel interviewed on the company's use of IT. Some inspection of systems took place where considered appropriate.

4. Structured interviews and a detailed questionnaire were used to elicit answers to more than 200 individual questions. For all applications, IT use was considered in terms of data capture, storage, manipulation and transmission. Companies' use of IT was noted, then scored. Companies were also asked to rate the importance of IT to a given activity within each of the process areas.

5. Responses were analysed through a simple scoring system. The results for applications of IT were plotted on a scatter graph, using maximum scores to denote best practice, against the scales of use and importance of IT in each of the six areas given above. Strategy, policy and procedures and degree of integration of IT were also

measured and plotted. The companies are not identified by name, though each has been advised of its result.

6. An *out-of-sector, best-in-class* company was identified on the fringe, so to speak, of the building and civil engineering sector. This engineering-construction company has established itself as a world leader in process plant and nuclear facility refurbishment works and has made substantial investments in IT and, more pertinent to this study, in integrating its systems.

7. The results show a wide variation in performance in the use of IT in construction site processes. The overall performance of the construction companies is such that two or three are positioned favourably in relation to both the industry average performance and best practice. For at least one construction company, the results do not appear good. Even so, it and indeed, all the other companies can take the results of this benchmarking study to help drive through investment in IT and related human resources.

8. An underlying theme in this study is that of activity and process integration. It is clear from the results that the construction companies have, for the main part, a long way to travel before they can reap the benefits from this tactic. Integration is essential, not simply because it represents the next technological challenge. Instead, integration should be seen in terms of bringing people closer together in their work.

9. The study has provided useful insights into IT use in construction site processes

624.0285'4
BEN